An elf has come to school! He is standing on Miss Smith's desk. "You can all have one wish," he says.

"I wish I had a parrot," says Dan.

The elf claps his hands. "Abracadabra!" he says. The next second, a parrot flies in!

"I wish I was rich," says Kevin.

"I wish I had wings," says Yasmin.

Meg wishes for a big pie and lots of chips.

Majid wishes for a forest!

"I wish I had a dragon," says Gwen.

A dragon flies in. It tries to get the parrot. Miss Smith has to tie it up.

"I wish I sat next to Patrick," says Ross.

But then Patrick says, "I wish I sat next to Callum."

Everyone gets a wish.

"Now Miss Smith must have a wish," says the elf. Miss Smith thinks. "I wish I had an extra hand!" she says.

The next second, Miss Smith has an extra hand. "Now I can do lots of things," she says.

"I must visit another school now," says the elf.

If the elf visits your school, what will you wish for?